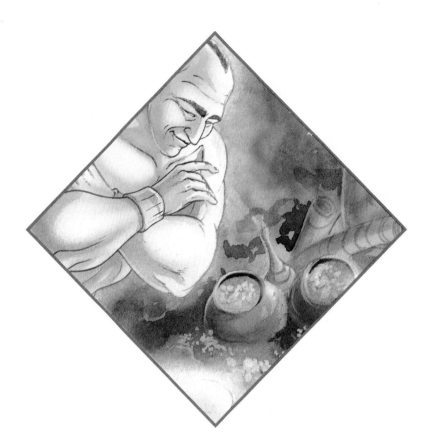

© 1995 Tormont Publications Inc., 338 St. Antoine Street East, Montreal, Quebec, Canada H2Y 1A3, Tel.: (514) 954-1441, Fax: (514) 954-5086

Illustrations: Zapp Graphic Design: Zapp Text: Carol Krenz

ISBN 2-89429-660-6 Printed in U.S.A.

ALADDIN
AND THE
MAGIC LAMP

ONCE upon a time, there was a widow who lived with her young son, Aladdin. They were very poor. So when a mysterious stranger offered to pay Aladdin a silver coin for a small favor, Aladdin was eager to earn it.

"What do you want me to do?" asked Aladdin.

"Follow me," the stranger replied.

THE stranger led Aladdin from the village into a nearby forest, where Aladdin often played. They stopped at the narrow entrance to a cave, which Aladdin had never seen before.

"I don't remember this cave," Aladdin said. "Has it always been here?"

The stranger did not answer him directly. Instead he said, "I want you to crawl inside, and find my old oil lamp. I would do it myself, only I'm too big to fit through the opening."

"All right," Aladdin said. "I'll look for it."

"And one more thing," the stranger added. "Don't touch anything else in there. Just find my oil lamp. Do you understand?"

The tone of the stranger's voice made Aladdin uncomfortable. For a moment, he thought about running away. But then he thought about the silver coin, and how much food his mother could buy with it.

"Don't worry," Aladdin said. "I'll find the lamp."

And he slipped into the narrow opening of the cave.

ONCE inside, Aladdin was surprised to find a dirty old oil lamp burning. It gave off just enough light for Aladdin to see that the cave was piled high with sparkling gold coins and precious jewels.

"If the stranger wants only a worthless lamp, he is either a fool or a Wizard," Aladdin said to himself. "And he does not appear to be a fool."

Just then, the Wizard thundered, "Give me my lamp!"

"All right, but let me come out first," Aladdin replied, and started to squeeze through the opening of the cave.

But the Wizard blocked the opening. "First give me the lamp!" he ordered.

"No!" Aladdin cried.

Suddenly, the Wizard's hand pushed Aladdin backwards into the cave. The Wizard was so angry that he did not realize a ring had fallen off his finger. It rolled to Aladdin's feet.

Then there was a groaning sound as the stranger pushed a large stone against the cave.

ATERRIBLE darkness surrounded Aladdin. He was terribly frightened. Was he trapped forever?

Not thinking what he was doing, he picked up the ring and slipped it on his finger. Then, Aladdin sat down to think how he might escape, idly twisting the ring round and round.

Suddenly, the cave filled with a pink light, and a smiling Genie appeared.

"I am the Genie of the ring. What is your wish, Master?" the Genie asked.

Aladdin was so astonished that for a moment he could not speak. Finally he said, "I'd like to go home."

IN A flash, Aladdin found himself at home, the old oil lamp still in his hand.

He gave it to his mother, and told her what had happened. "Well, it's not a silver coin," his mother said. "But I suppose we can clean it and use it."

But as she rubbed the lamp with her cloth, a second Genie appeared, even larger than the first. "I am the Genie of the lamp," the Genie said. "What is your command?"

Aladdin's mother clung to her son speechlessly, her eyes wide in disbelief.

Aladdin smiled shyly. "How about some dinner and Turkish delight for dessert?" he suggested.

Poof! It was done. The Genie produced trays and trays of hearty dishes and rare delicacies, more than Aladdin had tasted in all his years.

Aladdin and his mother ate well that day, and every day for several years. Aladdin grew tall and strong and his mother no longer had to work for other people. The Genie took care of all their simple needs. They were not a greedy family and asked for very little.

ONE DAY, when Aladdin had grown to become a handsome young man, he saw the Sultan's daughter in the market square. Halima was being carried grandly through the streets on her royal sedan, peeking curiously at the crowds.

Aladdin had one quick look at her face, and instantly made up his mind. He rushed home to tell his mother. "This is the happiest day of my life," he said, "for I have just seen the one woman in all the world I truly love."

His mother agreed to go to the Sultan and ask for Halima's hand in marriage. The Genie provided a small box of jewels for her to present at the Sultan's court.

The Sultan was impressed with the gift. But he said, "How do I know that your son has enough wealth to provide for my daughter properly all her life? Tell your son that to prove his worth, he must send me forty magnificent stallions bearing forty large boxes of just such gems as these, and forty warriors to escort them."

ALADDIN'S mother returned home with the news. "How can we possibly give the Sultan such riches?" she asked Aladdin.

"Well, perhaps the Genie of the lamp can help us," Aladdin replied.

As usual, the Genie smiled kindly, and instantly obeyed Aladdin's command.

Poof! Forty mighty horses pawed the ground impatiently. They carried magnificent boxes of huge rubies, sapphires, emeralds and diamonds. Forty mounted warriors with white turbans and wide scimitars awaited Aladdin's instructions.

"To the palace and the Sultan!" Aladdin announced proudly.

THE SULTAN was delighted with his great gifts, and realized how determined Aladdin was to win Halima. So Halima and Aladdin married, and Aladdin built a grand palace right next to the Sultan's, with the Genie's help, of course.

The Sultan was proud of his son-in-law and Halima loved her husband, who was kind and thoughtful, as well as generous.

BUT THE couple's peace was soon disturbed. One day the wicked Wizard returned to the town, disguised as a peddler.

"New oil lamps for old," he cried from window to window. People gladly traded in their dingy lamps for shiny new ones.

"Here," Halima called to him, "take mine as well," and she handed the stranger Aladdin's battered old lamp.

Aladdin had never told Halima the secret of the lamp, and now it was too late!

THE WIZARD rubbed the lamp eagerly and gave the Genie a command. In an instant, Halima and the palace were transported high, high into the air and whisked away to the Wizard's far-off land.

"Now you will be my wife!" the Wizard shouted with a cruel laugh. Poor Halima threw herself onto her bed cushions and wept bitterly.

ALADDIN returned home to find that his palace had disappeared, and his wife was nowhere to be found.

Quickly, he remembered the Wizard's ring, and rubbed it three times.

"Great Genie, what has happened to my wife and home?" Aladdin asked.

"The Wizard who shut you in a cave years ago has returned, Master," the Genie explained. "He has taken your palace, your wife and the magic lamp to his own country."

"Then I beg you, Genie, restore them all to me at once!" Aladdin pleaded.

"My powers are not strong enough," the Genie replied. "But I can take you to them."

It was, at least, a beginning.

IT WAS not long before Aladdin found himself in the dark halls of the Wizard's palace. He tiptoed softly from room to room, until he found Halima. Aladdin hugged her close, as she tried to explain what had happened.

"Shh! Say not one word," Aladdin whispered, "until we figure out how to escape."

So together they agreed on a plan. Halima would find a way to poison the Wizard. The Genie of the ring supplied the poison.

That night, Halima prepared the evening meal. Then she offered the Wizard a glass of wine, and smiled so deeply into his eyes that he drank every last drop. Soon he slumped over on the cushions. He was quite, quite dead.

ALADDIN ran into the room, pulled the oil lamp from the Wizard's pocket, and quickly rubbed it.

"I am happy to see my rightful master once more," the Genie smiled. "Shall we go home now?"

"At once!" said Aladdin, and the palace lifted high into the air and floated dreamily back to the Sultan's kingdom.

The Sultan and Aladdin's mother were overjoyed to see their children. A great feast was held for everyone in the kingdom to celebrate the couple's return.

Aladdin and Halima lived a long and happy life together and their smiles can still be seen every time you polish an old brass lamp!

ALI BABA
AND THE FORTY THIEVES

ONCE upon a time, in a city in Persia, there lived a man named Ali Baba. He and his wife were very poor. All day long, Ali Baba collected twigs in the forest, and sold them in bundles for firewood.

One day in the woods, Ali Baba heard the thundering sound of galloping horses approaching. Afraid that it might be robbers, Ali Baba hid up in a tree.

Sure enough, forty evil-looking men rode up right beneath Ali Baba.

The leader jumped off his horse next to a large rock set in the hillside, and commanded, "Open Sesame!"

The rock slowly moved, revealing a large cave. All forty thieves disappeared inside, carrying sacks of treasure.

Moments later they emerged, and the leader commanded, "Close Sesame!" The rock moved back into place, and the thieves rode off with much shouting and laughing.

ALI BABA could hardly believe what he had seen. Quickly, he scrambled out of the tree and ran to the rock.

"Open Sesame!" he cried with forced confidence.

The rock moved again, and Ali Baba stepped into the cave. Inside were great riches. Chests of jewels, bags of gold and silver coins, vases, trays, plates and heavy carpets were piled and scattered in a careless fashion.

"They won't notice if I take a few things," Ali Baba decided, and so he filled four sacks with gold nuggets and hurried back outside.

WHEN he got home, Ali Baba and Fatima, his wife, tried to count the coins, but there were far too many. Ali Baba hurried to borrow a coin measure from his rich brother Kassim. He arrived at Kassim's house breathless with excitement.

"What could you possibly have to count?" Kassim asked. "You are a very poor man."

"But tonight, I have new wealth," Ali Baba replied. Then he told Kassim about the cave. As he described the riches he had seen, Ali Baba noticed a gleam appear in Kassim's eyes.

"Are you sure no one saw you go inside the cave?" Kassim asked.

"Quite sure," Ali Baba said.

Now, Kassim was a greedy man who always wanted more money. So he went to the cave late that same night and cried, "Open Sesame!" just the way Ali Baba had done. Soon he had filled forty sacks with jewels and gold coins.

He was so busy stuffing his sacks that he didn't notice the sound of horses outside the cave. Kassim was trapped! The furious leader cut him to pieces, and left his body outside the cave.

Early the next morning, Kassim's wife ran to Ali Baba's house. "Have you seen my husband?" she asked.

"No, I haven't," Ali Baba replied. But he feared for Kassim. He hurried to the cave and discovered poor Kassim's body. Ali Baba wrapped the body in a carpet and took it home. But someone had to sew up the pieces before Kassim could be given a proper funeral.

Ali Baba did not want the thieves to find out who had taken Kassim's body. So he asked his trusted servant, Morgantina, to make the arrangements.

MORGANTINA went to the town cobbler, and asked him to sew the body together.

"I am prepared to pay you handsomely, but you must allow me to blindfold you," she said.

The cobbler agreed, and Morgantina led him blindfolded to Ali Baba's house.

"The cobbler will not be able to tell anyone where we live," Morgantina told Ali Baba. "So for the moment, we are safe."

When the cobbler had finished his gruesome job, he was again blindfolded, and Morgantina led him home.

BUT THE forty thieves soon realized someone else had discovered their cave. The leader sent one of his men to spy in the town. By chance, the thief asked the cobbler if he had seen anything interesting lately.

"I will talk for a small reward," the cobbler said.

So the thief paid the cobbler, and the cobbler told him about his strange sewing job.

"I can show you where I went, even though I was blindfolded, because I counted how many steps and how many turns I took," the cobbler said.

Sure enough, the cobbler led the thief to Ali Baba's house.

The thief quickly painted a red cross on the door, and rushed back to tell the others.

"We will kill Ali Baba and all his family tonight," the leader declared. "No one will ever disturb our cave again!"

IN THE meantime, Morgantina, who was as wise as she was pretty, saw the red cross on Ali Baba's door, and suspected a plot. Calmly, she painted red crosses on all the doors in the street.

That night, the forty thieves rode into town to kill Ali Baba. But every door was marked, and they could not tell which house was truly his. The leader was enraged.

"You fool!" he shouted at the thief who had marked Ali Baba's door. "You shall pay for your haste and your stupidity!" And then he killed him.

THE LEADER went himself to see the cobbler. And he paid the cobbler once again to show him Ali Baba's door. This time the leader memorized the exact house.

"I will not be fooled twice," he muttered.

The next morning, the leader bought thirty-nine large olive oil jars.

"Each of you, get in a jar," he ordered the remaining thieves. He poured olive oil in the last jar and then shut all the lids.

"Be quiet until you hear my command," he warned his men. "Then rush into the house and kill them all."

The jars were loaded onto a large cart, and the leader drove it to Ali Baba's home and knocked on the door.

"HOW MAY I help you?" asked Ali Baba, who did not recognize the leader of the thieves.

"I am an oil merchant," the man replied. "I see you have a large courtyard. Could I store my jars for the night?"

"Of course," Ali Baba said. "And we would be honored if you would eat supper with us."

The leader unloaded his jars in the courtyard, knocking once on each jar to let his men know they were now safely in the household of Ali Baba.

ORGANTINA was in the kitchen preparing the evening meal. When she heard that an oil merchant was staying as a guest, she decided to sample some of his olive oil.

To her horror, when she lifted the lid off a jar, a voice growled, "Is it time yet?"

"No," she muttered in a deep voice. Morgantina checked all the jars. She found a man hidden in every jar but one, and each time she said, "It's not time yet," in a deep voice.

Morgantina realized that the oil merchant was not what he claimed, and knew they were in great danger.

SHE DRAGGED the single jar containing oil into her kitchen. There, she heated it until it bubbled and boiled. Then, very carefully, Morgantina carried the boiling oil back out to the courtyard.

QUICKLY, she poured the boiling oil into the jars, and killed the thieves, one by one. Then she hurried back inside to find Ali Baba, who was entertaining his visitor.

"I would like to dance for our very special guest this evening, before he has his meal," Morgantina said.

"That would indeed be a rare treat," Ali Baba smiled.

S O MORGANTINA put on her finest robes and veils, and placed tiny cymbals on her fingers. Then she took a huge dagger and wrapped it carefully into the folds of her skirts so that no one could see it.

As Morgantina danced, the guests applauded her grace and beauty. She twirled and spun faster and faster, moving closer and closer to the thief, smiling at him through her soft veil.

SUDDENLY, she leapt upon the thief and plunged her knife into his heart!

"What have you done?" cried Ali Baba.

"His band of thieves was going to kill us all tonight," Morgantina explained.

Then she showed Ali Baba the jars with the dead men. Ali Baba recognized the thieves from the forest.

"My family and I are eternally indebted to you, my brave Morgantina," said Ali Baba.

Ali Baba shared the riches from the cave with Morgantina, who never had to work as a servant again. They used their wealth wisely and generously. And Ali Baba never mentioned the cave to anyone ever again.

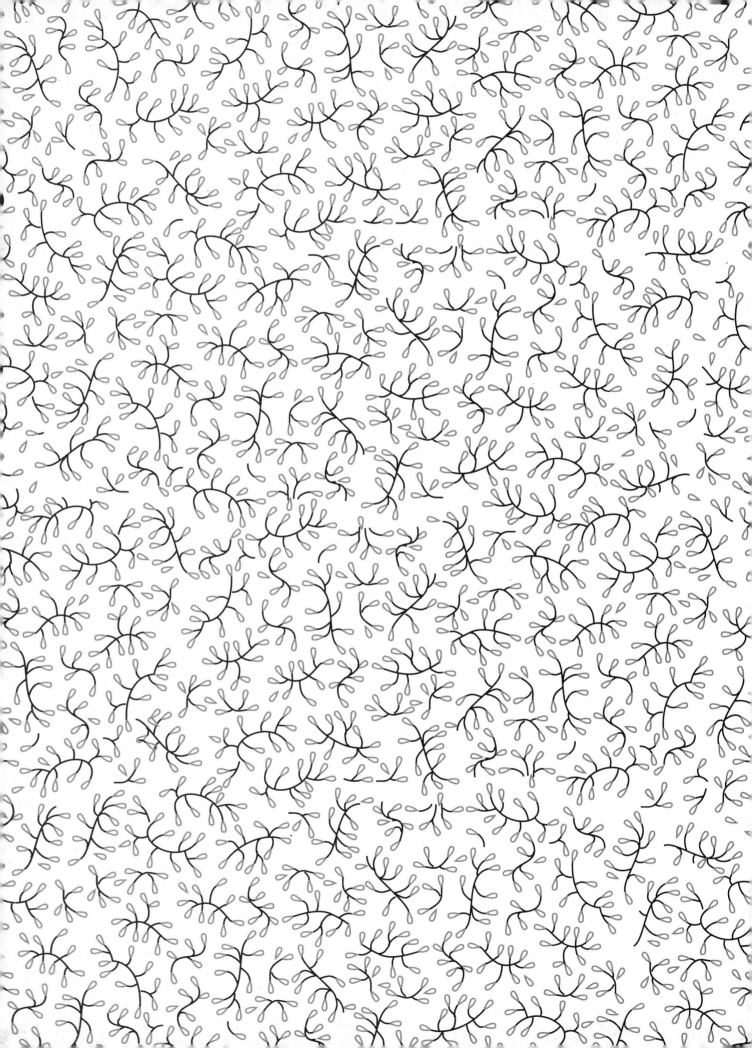